THE LOVE ONE ANO[THE]R BIBLE S[TUDY] [SE]RIES

FORGIVING
PURSUING RESTORATION
IN RELATIONSHIPS

A Bible Study by

Churches Alive!

MINISTERING TO THE CHURCHES OF THE WORLD
600 Meridian Avenue, Suite 200
San Jose, California 95126-3427

Published by

BRINGING TRUTH TO LIFE
NavPress Publishing Group
P.O. Box 35001, Colorado Springs, Colorado 80935

Cover photograph: Willard Clay
Interior cartoons: Bob Fuller

Printed in the United States of America

*Because we share kindred aims for helping local churches fulfill Christ's Great
Commission to "go and make disciples," NavPress and Churches Alive have
joined efforts on certain strategic publishing projects that are intended to bring
effective disciplemaking resources into the service of the local church.*

*For more than a decade, Churches Alive has teamed up with churches of all
denominations to establish vigorous disciplemaking ministries. At the same time,
NavPress has focused on publishing Bible studies, books, and other resources
that have grown out of The Navigators' 50 years of disciplemaking experience.*

*Now, together, we're working to offer special products like this one that are
designed to stimulate a deeper, more fruitful commitment to Christ in the local
gatherings of His Church.*

The LOVE ONE ANOTHER *series was written by Russ Korth, Ron Wormser, Jr., and
Ron Wormser, Sr. of Churches Alive. Many individuals from both Churches
Alive and NavPress contributed greatly in bringing this project to publication.*

Contents

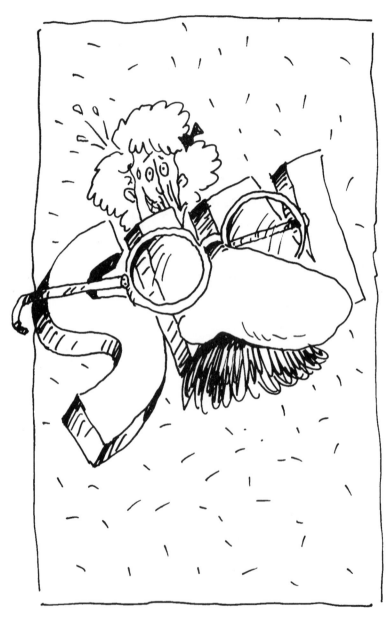

God's forgiveness is not a disguise to hide our sins.
It is complete. God takes away our sin,
condemnation and guilt.

God's Forgiveness

1 Think of a time as a child when you needed to be forgiven by your mother or your father. Consider how you felt until you had some assurance that you were forgiven. In what ways do you think your relationship with your parent at that time was like your relationship to God?

2 What do you think is one of the most important aspects of gaining forgiveness after you have done something wrong?

3 Each of the following passages has one or more terms associated with forgiveness. Choose at least one term from each passage, then write out a definition for each one you list.

TERM ASSOCIATED WITH FORGIVENESS	DEFINITION OF TERM FROM DICTIONARY
Romans 3:25	
Romans 4:5-7	
Ephesians 1:7	
1 John 1:9	

4 Which terms, if any, fulfill the aspect of forgiveness you listed in question 2?

5 Using the information from your chart in question 3, write your own definition of God's forgiveness.

6 Why is it important to understand God's forgiveness? (Ephesians 4:32)

7 Each of the passages below gives an illustration of the extent of God's forgiveness. Identify and explain each illustration.

Psalm 103:12

Isaiah 38:17

Micah 7:19

8 Read Isaiah 43:25 and Hebrews 10:17-18. What do you think is meant by the expression, "and I will not remember your sins"?

9 a. The verses examined in questions 7 and 8 clearly establish the fact of God's forgiveness. What are some things that help you feel forgiven by God?

b. What actions would you suggest to a person who did not feel forgiven by God?

c. In what ways do you think failing to feel forgiven by God would affect your life adversely?

Why God Forgives

▼

1 a. What are some possible reasons you think might motivate a person to forgive a financial debt?

    b. Which, if any, of the reasons you listed do you think might motivate God to forgive?

2 No matter what the reason, when someone forgives a financial debt, there is a cost involved—namely the money that is owed. Tell why or why not you think that there always is some cost to forgiving.

3 What cost did Christ incur to pay for your forgiveness? (Explain your answer.)

Matthew 26:26-28

2 Corinthians 5:21

4 Compare Jesus' payment for sin with the Old Testament sacrifices. (Hebrews 9:22-28)

JESUS' PAYMENT	OLD TESTAMENT SACRIFICES
HOW THEY ARE DIFFERENT	HOW THEY ARE THE SAME

5 What has Jesus' payment for sin accomplished for you? (Hebrews 10:11-14)

6 According to Hebrews 10:1-2, how should we feel about our past sins?

7 What does a nonChristian have to do to experience God's forgiveness? (Acts 26:18-20)

8 How is repentance described in Isaiah 55:6-7?

9 Read Psalm 32:1-5 and 1 John 1:8-10.

a. What should you do when you sin?

b. What attitudes are involved?

10 Under what circumstances is there a difference between failure to confess a sin and refusal to confess a sin? How does God treat you in each situation?

11 How can you continually live in fellowship with God? (1 John 1:7-9)

12 Choose one of the situations given below and explain how you would counsel the person having the guilt feelings.

- ☐ A lady traveling overseas "smuggled" a camera to a missionary by claiming it was hers as she went through customs. Later, her conscience began to bother her even though she had confessed to the Lord what she had done.
- ☐ A man confessed his sins as taught in 1 John 1:9. Later he developed a concern that he might not have remembered everything he should have confessed. He wondered if he still had unconfessed sin.

It isn't always easy to forgive, but God's forgiveness
of us is our pattern for forgiving others.

Forgiving Others

▼

1 According to West Virginia lore, the Hatfields and the McCoys had the longest family feud in the United States. In one version of the legend it began when a member of the Hatfield clan told the revenuers where they could find a McCoy still. Next thing you know, a McCoy took a shot at a Hatfield and pretty soon most of the members of both families were involved.

a. Why do you think a feud like this keeps on going for a long time?

b. What do you think it would take to stop a feud like this?

2 It would be very unusual for feuding church members to shoot at one another. What are some other ways deep hostilities are expressed among church members?

3 Why should you forgive others? (Colossians 3:12-13; KJV— "bowels" = "heart")

4 Read Matthew 18:21-22. Jewish tradition at the time of Christ was to forgive someone three times.

    a. Why do you think Peter asked this question?

    b. Write your interpretation of Jesus' answer to Peter.

5 Identify each of the major parts of the parable in Matthew 18:23-34.

IN THE PARABLE, THE . . . REPRESENTS
king
servant
10,000 talents
releasing of the debt
fellow-servant
100 denarii

You may want to use reference material to determine the current value of 10,000 talents and 100 denarii.

6 What is the main point of the parable? (Matthew 18:35)

7 What did Jesus say was the consequence of not forgiving others? (Matthew 6:14-15)

8 You are discussing forgiveness with one of your friends when he turns to you and says, "I'll never be able to forgive John after what he has done to me." What would you say to him?

9 Choose one of the situations presented, and answer the four questions.

☐ Your neighbor borrows your electric drill. When he returns it, it no longer works.
☐ You suspect another Christian of starting rumors about you.
☐ Your spouse continually uses you as the object of his or her jokes.
☐ Your sixteen-year-old daughter tells you she is pregnant.

a. How would you apply the scriptural teachings on forgiveness?

b. What would you do in this situation?

c. What effect would you hope your action would have?

d. If this effect didn't occur, what would you do?

LESSON FOUR
Results of Forgiving

▼

1 a. Other than getting clean, what do you like best about taking a shower or bath?

b. Forgiving is analogous to a shower or bath in that it restores a sullied situation to what it was before. Can you think of an analogy between forgiveness and your favorite aspect listed above?

2 In your relationships with others, what are some of the benefits you enjoy the most when you are forgiven for your misdeeds?

3 What benefits do you receive when you forgive others? (Mercy and kindness should be understood as forgiveness in this context.)

Psalm 18:25

Proverbs 11:17

Matthew 5:7

4 From Romans 12:17-21 identify some of the actions that reflect a forgiving spirit. Who do you think benefits from these actions?

5 What do you think would occur in your church if all the members practiced Colossians 3:13?

6 Why do you think it is important for a church to exercise both discipline as taught in 1 Corinthians 5:1-5 and forgiveness as taught in 2 Corinthians 2:6-8?

7 How do you think a church can express forgiveness to a repentant member?

8 What might happen if forgiveness by a church is withheld? (2 Corinthians 2:6-8)

9 Tell why you agree or disagree with this statement: "Forgiveness is essential for any degree of intimacy. If you don't need to forgive me, it is because you don't know me well."

Treated unfairly? Many say, "Don't get mad—get even!"
God says something quite different.

Perspective on Injustice

1 One day in elementary school Billy shot a spitwad at Sally. It missed her and hit Jenifer. Tommy told the teacher what Billy did. She misunderstood him and punished Willy instead.

Ignoring gender, which of the children in this story were you most like when you were in elementary school?

2 Suppose you are Willy's parent and he comes home and tells you what happened. What would you tell Willy?

3 How should you view the circumstances that come into your life?

Isaiah 46:8-11

Lamentations 3:37

4 Read Job 1:7-22.

a. How is God's control expressed in this situation?

b. What do you think Job's response in verses 21-22 indicates about his attitude?

c. Briefly describe a specific instance in your own life in which Job's response would have been appropriate.

5 What do you know about any injustice that you suffer? (Romans 8:28-29)

6 What was David's reaction to the insults he received from Shimei? (2 Samuel 16:5-13)

7 a. How does the command in 1 Thessalonians 5:18 relate to injustices you suffer?

b. How can you give thanks when you don't feel grateful?

8 On pages 22-23 is a list of events in the life of Joseph from his boyhood to his later years. Reviewing these experiences illustrates how one person responded to injustices.

a. Mark those instances in which you think Joseph suffered injustice.

☐ Favored by father (Genesis 37:3-4)
☐ Dreams of leadership (Genesis 37:5-11)
☐ Brothers conspire to kill (Genesis 37:18-24)
☐ Sold into slavery (Genesis 37:25-28)
☐ Made head of household (Genesis 39:1-6)
☐ Imprisoned (Genesis 39:7-20)
☐ Given authority over prisoners (Genesis 39:21-23)

☐ Prophesies to two men (Genesis 40:1-22)
☐ Remembered after two years (Genesis 41:1-13)
☐ Interprets Pharaoh's dream (Genesis 41:14-36)
☐ Put in charge of Egypt's crops (Genesis 41:37-48)
☐ Reveals himself to brothers (Genesis 45:1-6)
☐ Reunited with father (Genesis 46:29-34)

b. What was Joseph's attitude during his lifetime? (Genesis 50:15-21)

c. How did these injustices relate to the leadership position God revealed to him in dreams? (Genesis 45:4-8)

9 What, in your opinion, is the overall lesson to be learned from Joseph's life?

10 a. How can you keep from being discouraged when you are treated unfairly? (Hebrews 12:1-4; KJV—"compassed" = "surrounded")

b. Why will this keep you from being discouraged? (Verse 2)

11 Review your answer to question 2. Would you change your response now? If so, to what?

Reacting to Injustice

1 For each of the five types of suffering listed, give one example from your life.

a. Suffering as a result of doing something wrong.

b. Suffering as a result of doing something foolish.

c. Suffering that has no relationship to human activity.

d. Suffering because another has done something wrong or foolish.

e. Suffering because you have done something right.

2 For which of the categories above could you give an example from the life of Jesus?

3 Study 1 Peter 2:19-25 and answer the following questions.

a. What should be your reaction when you suffer an injustice? (verses 19-20; KJV—"buffeted" = "beaten")

b. For what reasons should you react this way? (verses 20-21)

c. This passage mentions four things Jesus did not do when He suffered unjustly. List each one, and give a practical way you can follow His example.

JESUS DID NOT	HOW TO FOLLOW HIS EXAMPLE
Verse 22	
Verse 23	

d. What *did* Jesus do? (Verse 23)

e. How does Jesus' reaction relate to His view of God's sovereignty?

4 Describe a situation in your life in which applying James 1:2-4 would have been helpful. (KJV—"wanting" = "lacking")

5 a. What do you think you should do if a Christian defrauds you? (1 Corinthians 6:1-8)

b. What do you think you should do if a nonChristian defrauds you?

6 How can suffering injustices help you have an impact on others' lives? (1 Peter 3:13-18; KJV—"conversation" = "manner of life," "quickened" = "made alive")

7 a. Check all the situations where you feel you are often treated unfairly.

☐ While driving
☐ At work
☐ From my spouse
☐ Other (name it):

b. Evaluate your typical reaction for each situation you checked.

c. According to your study, what would be the proper way to respond?

d. Complete this sentence: *I can expect God's power to enable me to do this because. . . .*

An unforgiving spirit reveals itself in
many ways—often with unfortunate results.

Results of an Unforgiving Spirit

▼

---

1 If someone does something that upsets you, what animal would you be most like before you forgave the offender? Explain.

2 a. What attitudes and actions are not compatible with a for-giving spirit? (Ephesians 4:31-32)

   b. Of these things, list the two or three that are a potential problem for you.

   c. This week create your own study by answering only the questions that correspond to your list of potential problems.

3 Using a dictionary or other reference material, define "bitterness."

4 What are some things associated with bitterness? (Romans 3:13-14)

5 In your opinion, what are the major reasons people become bitter?

6 a. What failure can open the door to bitterness? Explain your answer. (Hebrews 12:14-15)

    b. In verse 15, why do you think bitterness is likened to a root?

7 a. Complete this short study on anger by filling in the chart. (Not all verses have answers in all sections.)

CHARACTERISTICS OF ANGER	RESULTS OF ANGER	WHAT ANGER REVEALS	CHARACTERISTICS OF A PERSON WHO IS SLOW TO ANGER
Proverbs 14:29			
Proverbs 16:32			
Proverbs 19:11			
Proverbs 22:24-25			
Proverbs 25:28			
Ecclesiastes 7:9			

b. As you read each column vertically, what conclusions do you draw?

8 a. What practical suggestions does James give to avoid anger? (James 1:19)

b. Why do you think these suggestions work?

9 Use a dictionary or other reference material to define "vengeance."

10 Rewrite Proverbs 20:22 in your own words. (KJV—"recompense" = "repay")

11 Why should you not seek vengeance? (Romans 12:17-21)

12 Using a dictionary or other reference material, define "clamor."

13 What kinds of behavior are associated with clamor?

John 19:15-16

Acts 22:22-25

14 a. What reaction did Solomon have to clamor? (Proverbs 21:19)

b. What are your reactions to clamor?

15 Why is slander (or evil speaking) so dangerous? (James 3:2-10)

16 Proverbs 26:18-28 identifies various sinful practices. List the ones which could be forms of slander. (KJV—"dissembleth" = "disguises")

17 Using a dictionary or other reference material, define "malice."

18 How are the concepts of "malice" and "forgiveness" expressed in Zechariah 7:9-10?

19 What will a continuous malicious attitude produce in your life? (Micah 2:1)

20 Write a summary of the teaching of each of the following verses. After completing all the summaries, draw a line from each summary to the malicious thought it describes.

Proverbs 3:29   *I'm glad she suffered.*

Proverbs 24:17-18   *I want to hurt him.*

Proverbs 26:24-25   *I'll be nice to him now, but. . . .*

Trying to ignore offenses without dealing with them
in a scriptural manner is like camping in a cactus patch.
Sooner or later, it'll get to you.

LESSON EIGHT
Offending Others
▼

1 Can you think of a time when someone was offended by you for something that wasn't your fault? Explain briefly.

2 Why do you think it is important to know about offenses? (Matthew 18:7-9)

3 What are some possible consequences of offenses?

Proverbs 18:19

2 Corinthians 6:3

4 What are some of the "excuses" people give for not becoming Christians which indicate they may have been offended?

5 Read Paul's statement in Romans 14:20-21, then rewrite it as you think Paul might say the same thing today.

6 Why do you think Jesus considered it to be so bad to offend a child? (Matthew 18:2-6)

7 a. What did Peter do that offended Jesus? (Matthew 16:21-23)

b. How might the same problem offend someone today?

8 a. What responsibility do you have when you've offended another? (Matthew 5:23-24)

b. What priority is indicated in this passage?

c. What steps do you think you should take to be reconciled to another?

10 What are some things you can do to avoid offending others?

1 Corinthians 10:32-33

Philippians 1:10

LESSON NINE
Being Offended

▼

1 a. Briefly describe a time as a youth when a friend talked you into doing something that got you into trouble.

b. Being encouraged to do something wrong is one kind of offense. What are some other types of offense?

2 a. What are the instructions you should follow if someone offends you? (Matthew 18:15-17)

b. What results are you hoping to gain by following these instructions? (verse 15)

3 From your experience, do you know any situation in which the instructions of the following passages were obeyed with the result that further steps were not necessary? If so, briefly describe the situation and the outcome.

Matthew 18:15

Matthew 18:16

4 What should your attitude be when someone offends you and asks forgiveness? (Luke 17:1-4)

5 What would you think of a person whose actions are described in Luke 17:4?

6 Study the account of Paul and Barnabas in Acts 12:25; 13:1-5,13; 15:36-41. Now answer the following questions.

a. Who was offended?

b. Who committed the offense?

c. What caused the offense?

d. How was the offense handled?

e. Would you suggest handling it differently? If so, how? If not, why not?

7 What are some of the consequences of not dealing with offenses in the church fellowship? (Do not give specific examples here or in your discussion.)

8 What action can you take that can help keep you from being offended by others? (Psalm 119:165)

NOTES AND PRAYER REQUESTS

NOTES AND PRAYER REQUESTS

Notes and Prayer Requests

NOTES AND PRAYER REQUESTS

If you enjoyed this study, you'll want to check out the other titles in the LOVE ONE ANOTHER series:

COMMUNICATING: Conveying Truth with Love
CONTRIBUTING: Helping Others Fulfill Their Potential
DEVELOPING UNITY: Upholding the Oneness God Gives Me
    with Others
FORGIVING: Pursuing Restoration in Relationships
HONORING: Holding Others in High Regard
UNDERSTANDING: Approaching Things from Another's Point
    of View
SUBMITTING: Letting God Use Others to Lead Me
LEADER'S GUIDE: Lead Your Group to Closer Personal
    Relationships

SMALL-GROUP MATERIALS FROM NAVPRESS

BIBLE STUDY SERIES

CRISISPOINTS FOR WOMEN
DESIGN FOR DISCIPLESHIP
GOD IN YOU
GOD'S DESIGN FOR THE FAMILY
INSTITUTE OF BIBLICAL
  COUNSELING SERIES

LIFECHANGE
LIFESTYLE SMALL GROUP SERIES
LOVE ONE ANOTHER
STUDIES IN CHRISTIAN LIVING
THINKING THROUGH DISCIPLESHIP

TOPICAL BIBLE STUDIES

Becoming a Woman of
  Excellence
Becoming a Woman of Freedom
The Blessing Study Guide
Celebrating Life
Growing in Christ
Growing Strong in God's Family
Homemaking
Intimacy with God

Loving Your Husband
Loving Your Wife
A Mother's Legacy
Surviving Life in the Fast Lane
To Run and Not Grow Tired
To Walk and Not Grow Weary
What God Does When Men Pray
When the Squeeze Is On

BIBLE STUDIES WITH COMPANION BOOKS

Bold Love
From Bondage to Bonding
Hiding from Love
Inside Out
The Masculine Journey
The Practice of Godliness
The Pursuit of Holiness

Secret Longings of the
  Heart
Transforming Grace
Trusting God
What Makes a Man?
The Wounded Heart
Your Work Matters to God

RESOURCES

Curriculum Resource Guide
How to Lead Small Groups
Jesus Cares for Women
The Small Group Leaders
  Training Course

Topical Memory System (KJV/NIV
  and NASB/NKJV)
Topical Memory System: Life
  Issues (KJV/NIV and
  NASB/NKJV)

VIDEO PACKAGES

Abortion
Bold Love
Hope Has Its Reasons
Inside Out

Living Proof
Parenting Adolescents
Unlocking Your Sixth Suitcase
Your Home, A Lighthouse

Churches Alive!

This study is just one item in a wide range of small group material authored by Churches Alive. Continue your study with other books in this series.

Churches Alive has local representatives who provide their own living expenses to serve you at your church. On-site support and training conferences will develop commitment and vision in group leaders. Our experienced staff can help you develop leaders, enrich your groups, and reach out to others.

Conferences and Support Services

A Pastor's Perspective:

"Churches Alive was a tremendous help to us when we were getting started in our discipleship ministry. We had to make a choice—either try to learn ourselves and make a lot of mistakes, or get some help and minimize mistakes. Their careful but goal-oriented approach helps any church build a solid, perpetuating ministry."

Churches Alive!
600 Meridian Avenue
Suite 200
San Jose, CA 95126
(408) 294-6000
(408) 294-6029 FAX

Conferences

Designed to strengthen the effectiveness of your leaders, our conferences and seminars range from one to four days. Most are taught by Churches Alive staff and local pastors. In addition, we arrange special seminars in your church to encourage people in your church to study the Bible.

Support Services

In dozens of denominations, our staff helps churches large and small. We can help you evaluate, plan, train leaders, and expand your small groups. Invite a Churches Alive representative to explore small group discipleship at your church.

Call 1-800-755-3787